No time to waste! Build the minifigure of
Hermione and turn the page!

Be careful with Time-Turners! Help Hermione keep everything the same by spotting ten differences in Hagrid's Hut.

Match the fragments to the witch or wizard by
writing the numbers in the correct circles.

1 2 3 4 5

Use your pens or pencils to create a potion.
Make it look really magical!

Who will have the next dance with Hermione at the Yule Ball? Read the clues and tick the answer.

THIS PERSON IS NOT WEARING GLASSES OR A BLACK SUIT. HIS CLOTHES HAVE RED ELEMENTS, BUT HIS HAIR DOES NOT.

Find the three sequences of Hogwarts founders below in the grid.

Find two picture pieces that don't match the Yule Ball photo.

1

2

3

4

5

6

7

Find three identical portraits of each founder of Hogwarts. Outline each founder in a different colour.

Help Hermione find her wand below, so she can free Harry and Ron from the Devil's Snare.

What's happening in front of Hagrid's hut? Look carefully at the picture to answer the questions.

1. In which squares can you see Hagrid?

2. The friends need to watch out for the executioner. Which square is he in?

3. In which squares are the doors to Hagrid's hut?

4. In which squares can you see pumpkins?

5. Show Hermione the square in which she can unfasten Buckbeak's chain from the post.

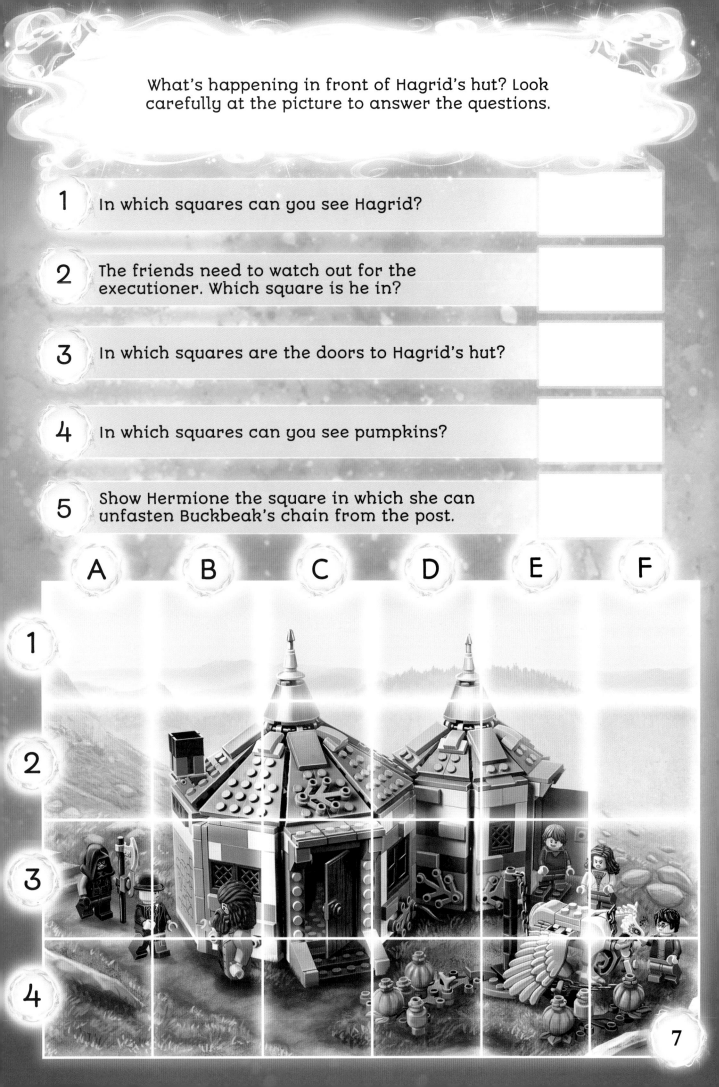

Even Hermione makes mistakes sometimes. The Polyjuice Potion she took turned her into ... a cat! Draw Hermione's new look.

Circle the objects you can use in a game
of Quidditch.

Join the sets of dots to reveal Cedric Diggory's
house animal.

Harry and Hermione have saved an innocent being! Help Buckbeak soar to safety through the maze of clouds.

START

FINISH

What is the spell to create light at the tip of a wand? Find the correct letters in the grid.

	A	B	C	D
1	K	R	C	M
2	L	X	Z	W
3	Y	U	O	V
4	B	R	S	G

2A   3B   1D   3C   4C

Find two identical characters in neighbouring groups. Match different characters into pairs each time.

Follow the clues and colour in the magical books.

1. The biggest book is not green.

2. The red book is medium size and it's next to the brown book.

3. The smallest book is yellow and the green book is next to it.

Help Luna Lovegood match the books into pairs.

How well do you know Gryffindor? Answer these questions by the Ghost of Gryffindor to find out!

1. Which of the words below best describes a true Gryffindor?

○ cheerful   ○ proud   ○ brave

2. Who is a Gryffindor student?

○ Luna   ○ Ginny   ○ Draco

3. What is a Gryffindor's favourite colour?

○ red   ○ blue   ○ green

4. Which object belonged to Godric Gryffindor?

○ cup   ○ sword   ○ diadem

Spot six differences between the two pictures of Harry's first Triwizard Tournament challenge.

Hermione and Ron seem like total opposites! Draw a line between the opposite words.

WIZARD   •   •   DEATH EATER

AUROR   •   •   PATRONUS

DUMBLEDORE   •   •   MUGGLE

DEMENTOR   •   •   VOLDEMORT

Count how many pumpkins there are around Hagrid's hut.

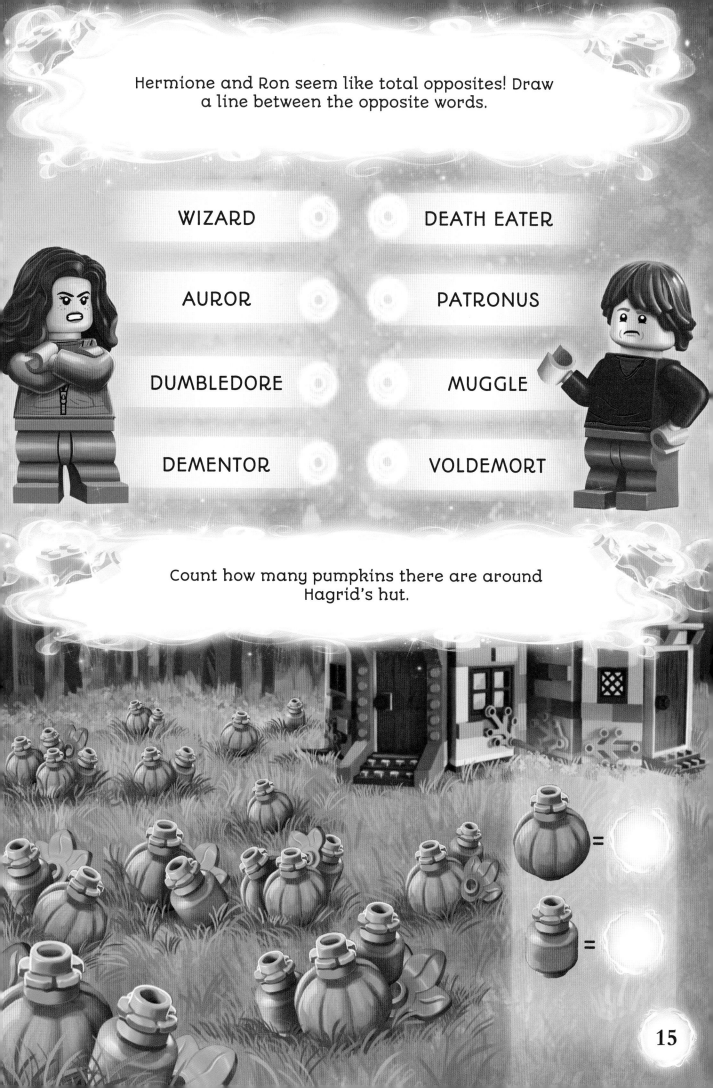

=

=

Hermione is not keen on Divination class. Draw what she might see in the magic crystal ball.

Hermione knows what a Hufflepuff's traits are. Do you? Follow the arrows. The numbers indicate how many steps to go in that direction.

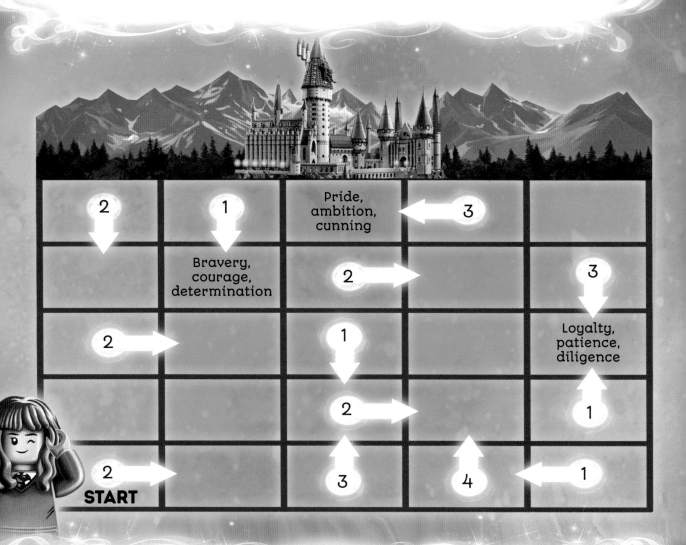

Has Hermione lost the Time-Turner? Match the identical objects. The one without a match is hers.

Find Harry's Christmas present! It's not green but has yellow bits with no envelope attached to it.

LOOK CLOSELY!

Hermione is a bit over-prepared for Christmas! Mark the objects she will need.

Who was the hungriest at Christmas lunch?
Untangle the lines then circle the person who
chose the biggest portion.

Follow Harry's Quidditch tips to fly across the
pitch and send the Quaffle through the goalpost.

1. Start at field 5B and fly one
field left, then one field up to be next to
your teammate.

2. In order to avoid being knocked by the Bludgers, fly
to field 2A.

3. Fly to field 2B, then quickly to 3B! Wow! The Beater almost
got you!

4. Next fly to 3C and one field up. Then throw the Quaffle
through the hoop in field 1C.

5. Now, you've got five seconds to find the
Golden Snitch. Start now!

Colour in the Hungarian Horntail for Harry, so he knows what will be chasing him in the first task of the Triwizard Tournament.

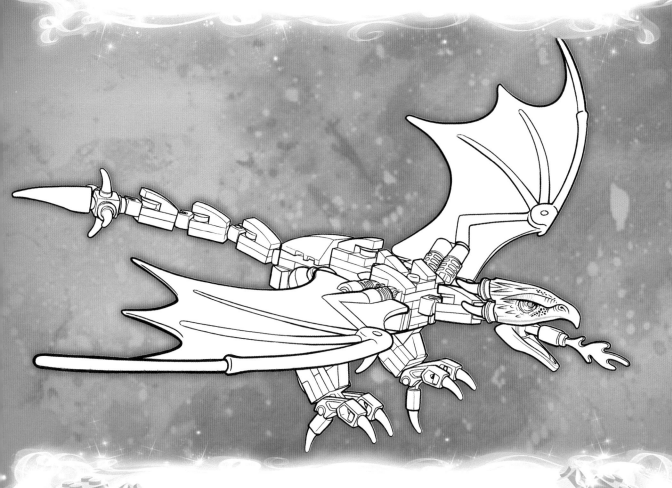

Cross out every other letter to find out what the most important traits of a Slytherin are.

AKMWBOIRTBIDOMNT

RYEVSPOWUARSCGERFKUBLANIEFSDSA

CWUPNSNRIONUGA

Follow Hagrid's orders to help the Beauxbatons Academy of Magic's carriage land safely.

FINISH

22

Which portraits of Harry and Ron should appear
in the places with question marks?

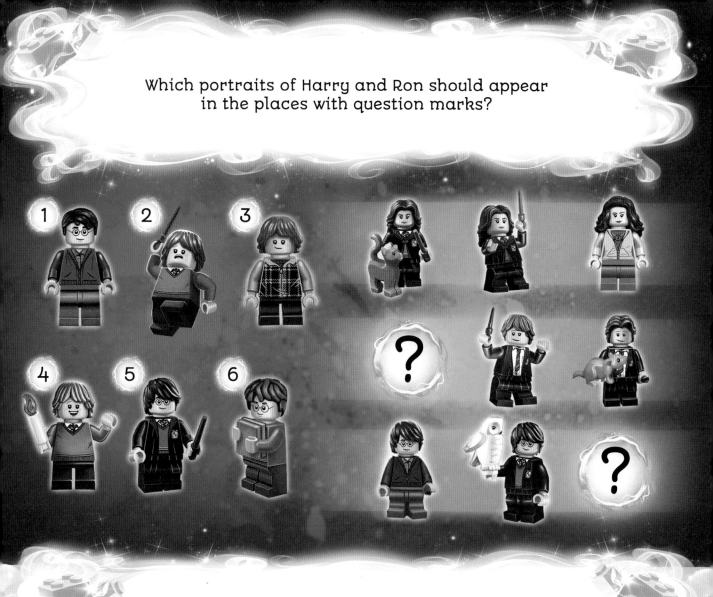

Use your pens or pencils to see what will appear
when Malfoy says, "*Serpensortia!*"

Untangle the lines to match the magical artefacts with their descriptions.

1 An object used to review memories.

2 An object that shows the deepest desire of one's heart.

3 An object or a creature in which a Dark wizard or witch has hidden a fragment of their soul.

4 An object enchanted to instantly teleport someone to a specific location.

Cast the Patronus Charm and guide its beam using straight lines so that it reaches all the Dementors.

START

Colour in the Knight bus that takes Harry to the
Leaky Cauldron.

Which portrait of the Malfoy family is their
mirror reflection?

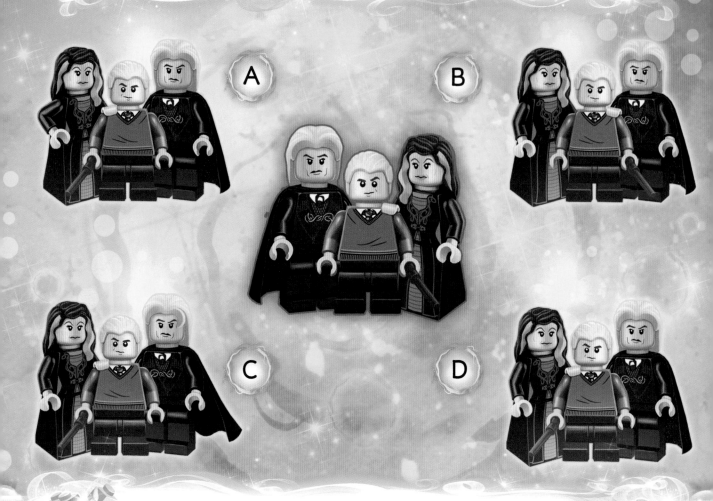

A

B

C

D

Which potion bottle should be next? It's important
to choose the right one, as Hermione needs to use
this substance in her Potions class.

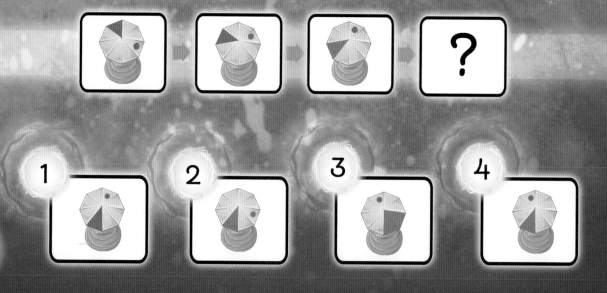

1

2

3

4

Use Harry's clues to help find Sirius Black, who's been attacked by Dementors. Write the correct number in the circle.

LOOK FOR THE PLACE WITH TWO TREES, MORE THAN TWO STONES AND LESS THAN THREE BUSHES.

Look at the feathers Hermione has levitated and mark the one she is concentrating on.

There are many magical creatures and objects at Hogwarts. Mark the odd one out in each row.

Are there more brown or black spiders? It makes no difference to Ron, he likes neither type! Count them and write the correct numbers in the circles below.

Match the characters with their animal companions. Try matching the shaded bars if you need help.

1

2

3

4

5

Answers

pp. 2–3

4

5

3

2

1

pp. 4–5

3

5

pp. 6–7

1	3B 4B	4	4D 4E 4F
2	3A	5	3E
3	3C 4C 2E 3E		

p. 9

pp. 10–11

LUMOS

p. 12

p. 14

p. 13

1	brave	3	red
2	Ginny	4	sword

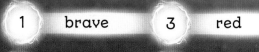